Mura Cha Ch

GOOD VIBES ADULT COLORING BOOK

Never Give Up

Find out the cat if you can

Join Our Newsletter To Get
50 Free Coloring Pages

https://mulachacha.com/readerfree/

Color Testing Chart

Mula Cha Cha

Mufa Cha Cha

Mula Cha Cha

Mu a Cha Cha

Mula Cha Cha

Mula Cha Cha

Mula Cha Cha

Mula Cha Cha

Mu a Cha Cha

Mula Cha Cha

Mula Cha Cha

Mula Cha Cha

Mula Cha Cha

Mu͡ta Cha Cha

Mula Cha Cha

Mu a Cha Cha

Mula Cha Cha

Mu a Cha Cha

Mula Cha Cha

Mula Cha Cha

Mu(a Cha Cha

Mula Cha Cha

Mula Cha Cha

Mula Cha Cha

Mula Cha Cha

Mula Cha Cha

Mula Cha Cha

Mua Cha Cha

Mura Cha Cha

Mufa Cha Cha

Mula Cha Cha

Mula Cha Cha

Mura Cha Cha

Mula Cha Cha

Mu a Cha Cha

Mula Cha Cha

Mu a Cha Cha

Mua Cha Cha

Mula Cha Cha

Mula Cha Cha

Mu Fa Cha Cha

Mula Cha Cha

Mula Cha Cha

Mula Cha Cha

Mu a Cha Cha

Mula Cha Cha

Mula Cha Cha

GIFT CARDS

Get More Books

Mua Cha Cha

Write A Review
It Means A Lot To Mula Cha Cha

"Hey, if you like this book, will you please leave a review?
Even a few sentences really helps. "

"Tell Us What Sections Did You Like? "

"Tell Us What You Feel About Quotes?"

f mulachacha.coloringbooks

Scan
to discover !

mulachacha.coloringbooks

Scan
to discover !

Printed in the USA
CPSIA information can be obtained
at www.ICGtesting.com
LVHW081654200624
783545LV00010B/234